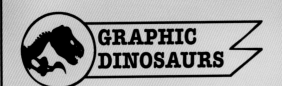

GRAPHIC DINOSAURS

presents

ANKYLOSAURUS

THE ARMOURED DINOSAUR!

ILLUSTRATED BY NICK SPENDER

BOOK HOUSE

Graphic Dinosaurs Ankylosaurus
was produced by
David West Children's Books
7 Princeton Court
55 Felsham Road
London SW15 1AZ

Designed and written by David West
Illustrated by Nick Spender and David West
Consultant: Steve Parker, Senior Scientific Fellow, Zoological Society of London
Cover designed by Rob Walker

First published in the UK in MMX by Book House,
an imprint of The Salariya Book Company Ltd.,
25, Marlborough Place, Brighton BN1 1UB

Please visit the Salariya Book Company at:
www.book-house.co.uk

1 3 5 7 9 8 6 4 2

ISBN: 978-1-907184-00-0 (HB)
ISBN: 978-1-907184-01-7 (PB)

A CIP catalogue record for this book is available from the British Library.

Photographic credits:
5t, luc legay; 5m, goldmund100; 5b, Vall; 30 both, coolisandsong24

Printed and bound in China.

Printed on paper from sustainable sources.

CONTENTS

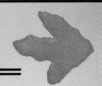

WHAT IS AN ANKYLOSAURUS?

ANKYLOSAURUS MEANS 'STIFFENED LIZARD'

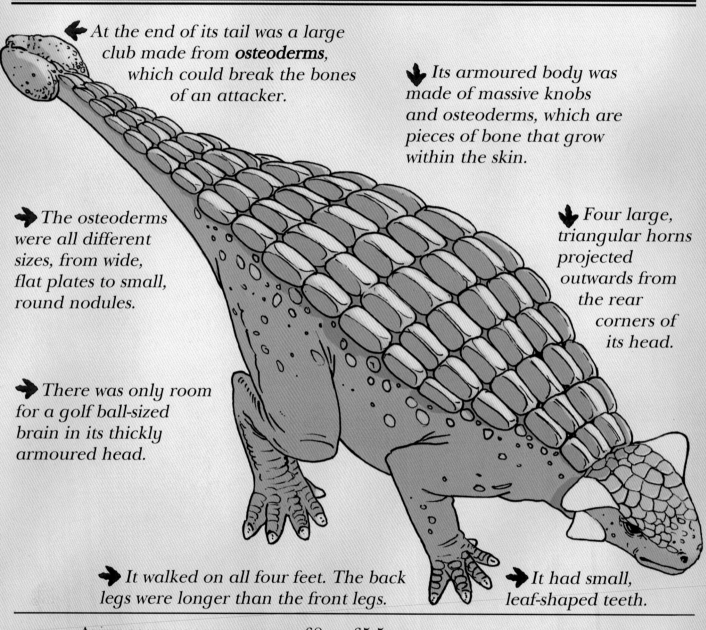

At the end of its tail was a large club made from **osteoderms**, which could break the bones of an attacker.

Its armoured body was made of massive knobs and osteoderms, which are pieces of bone that grow within the skin.

The osteoderms were all different sizes, from wide, flat plates to small, round nodules.

Four large, triangular horns projected outwards from the rear corners of its head.

There was only room for a golf ball-sized brain in its thickly armoured head.

It walked on all four feet. The back legs were longer than the front legs.

It had small, leaf-shaped teeth.

ANKYLOSAURUS LIVED AROUND 68 TO 65.5 MILLION YEARS AGO, DURING THE **CRETACEOUS PERIOD. FOSSILS** OF ITS SKELETON HAVE BEEN FOUND IN NORTH AMERICA (SEE PAGE 30).

The adult Ankylosaurus measured up to 8 metres long, 2 metres high and 2 metres wide. It weighed about 4,536 kilogrammes.

A Nile crocodile

PLATE ARMOUR

Ankylosaurus is one of the best-known armoured dinosaurs. Bony plates embedded in its tough, scaly skin protected the animal from the sharp teeth of predators like Tyrannosaurus. The armoured skin was similar to that of today's crocodiles.

SMALL BRAIN

Although Ankylosaurus had a small brain, it had a good sense of smell. This was useful to sniff out the flowering plants it fed on.

Its brain was not much bigger than a golf ball.

FLOWER POWER

Ankylosauruses lived right up until the **extinction** event 65.6 million years ago, at the end of the Cretaceous period. This event was probably due to a large **meteor** or **comet** hitting our planet, causing the climate to change. Dinosaurs became extinct in a very short time.

The Cretaceous period had seen a huge increase in flowering plants and **pollinating** insects, such as bees. This led to an increase in the number and types of plant eaters, such as Ankylosaurus.

PART ONE

THE RIVER

DAY BREAKS OVER WESTERN LAURASIA (TODAY'S NORTH AMERICA). IT IS THE FINAL STAGE OF THE LATE CRETACEOUS PERIOD, AROUND 66 MILLION YEARS AGO.

YARK

YARK

YARK

ABOVE THE GRAZING ANKYLOSAURUSES, SMALL BIRDS CALLED ICHTHYORNIS FLY OUT TO THEIR FEEDING GROUNDS AT SEA.

THE BIRDS' NOISY CALLS DRAW THE ATTENTION OF A YOUNG ANKYLOSAURUS. IT LOOKS UP.

YARK

YARK

SPLAT

IT NOTICES THAT THERE ARE TWO BRIGHT LIGHTS IN THE SKY INSTEAD OF ONE.

THE OTHER LIGHT IS A COMET CLOSE TO EARTH. ITS BODY LEAVES A TRAIL OF VAPOUR THAT REFLECTS THE SUN'S LIGHT. IT WOULD POSE A THREAT TO ALL LIFE ON EARTH IF IT WERE TO COLLIDE WITH THE PLANET.

ON EARTH, THE CLIMATE IS WARM AND HUMID. THE ANKYLOSAURUSES MAKE THEIR WAY DOWN TO A RIVER, WHERE THE BANKS ARE CROWDED WITH JUICY, LOW-LYING PLANTS. THEY PASS A TRICERATOPS, A PLANT-EATING DINOSAUR WITH THREE LARGE HORNS. IT IS BUSY FEEDING ON THE PLANTS WITH ITS BEAK-LIKE MOUTH.

MANY OF THE PLANTS HAVE FLOWERS. BEES BUZZ FROM FLOWER TO FLOWER, HELPING TO POLLINATE THEM AS THEY GATHER THE NECTAR.

8

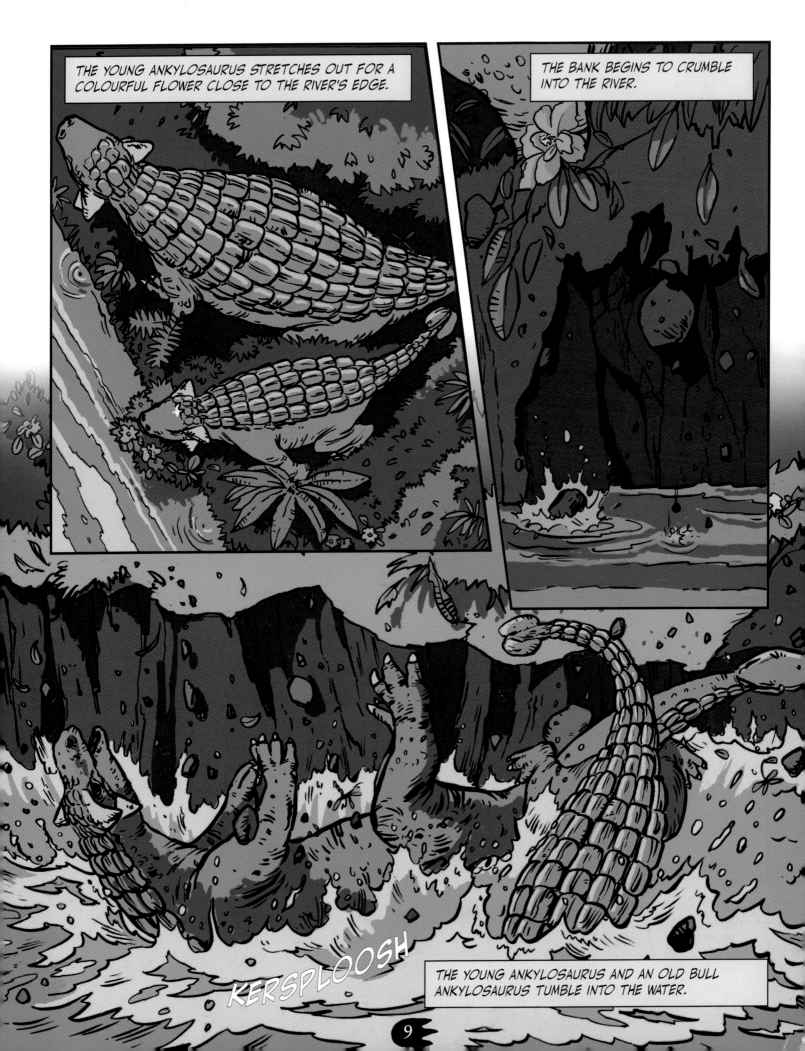

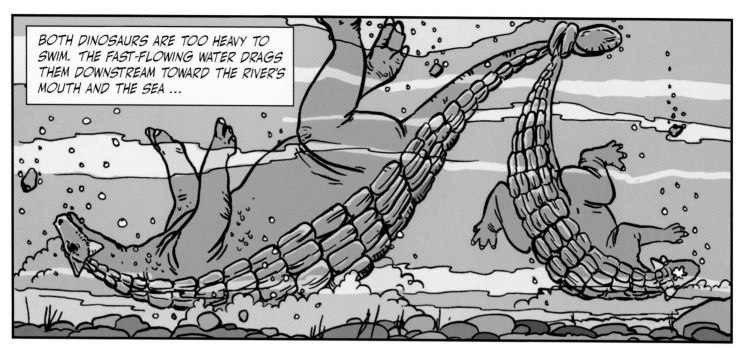

BOTH DINOSAURS ARE TOO HEAVY TO SWIM. THE FAST-FLOWING WATER DRAGS THEM DOWNSTREAM TOWARD THE RIVER'S MOUTH AND THE SEA ...

...WHERE THEY ARE BOTH WASHED UP ONTO A LARGE GRAVEL BANK, SPLUTTERING AND COUGHING UP WATER.

COUGH

GROUGH

NONE THE WORSE FOR THEIR DIP, THE ANKYLOSAURUSES HEAD FOR THE BANK. NEARBY, A DARK SHAPE BREAKS THE SURFACE OF THE MUDDY ESTUARY WATER.

A GROUP OF YOUNG ORNITHOMIMUSES RACES PAST THE TWO LUMBERING ANKYLOSAURUSES. THESE SWIFT-RUNNING DINOSAURS HAVE POWERFUL REAR LEGS AND A LONG TAIL FOR BALANCE. THEY HAVE COME TO DRINK FROM THE WATER'S EDGE.

THERE IS A SUDDEN MOVEMENT AND A SPLASH. A GIANT CROCODILE CALLED A DEINOSUCHUS ATTACKS ONE OF THE YOUNG ORNITHOMIMUSES.

SKREEEK

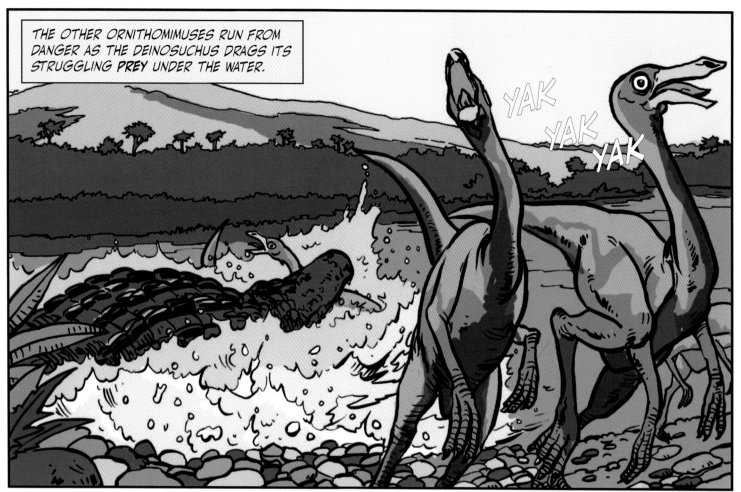

THE OTHER ORNITHOMIMUSES RUN FROM DANGER AS THE DEINOSUCHUS DRAGS ITS STRUGGLING **PREY** UNDER THE WATER.

BENEATH THE SURFACE, THE GIANT CROCODILE CARRIES ITS DROWNED VICTIM TO ITS DEN UNDER THE BANK.

THE TWO ANKYLOSAURUSES ARE NOW ON THE OPPOSITE BANK FROM THE REST OF THE GROUP. THE YOUNGSTER IS UNCERTAIN WHAT TO DO.

THE YOUNG ANKYLOSAURUS IS DISTRACTED BY A BEE BUZZING PAST. WHERE THERE ARE BEES, THERE ARE FLOWERING PLANTS.

BZZZZZZZ

THE OLD BULL LUMBERS OFF TO A PATCH OF RICH UNDERGROWTH AND SO THE YOUNG ANKYLOSAURUS FOLLOWS WITH A GRUMBLING STOMACH.

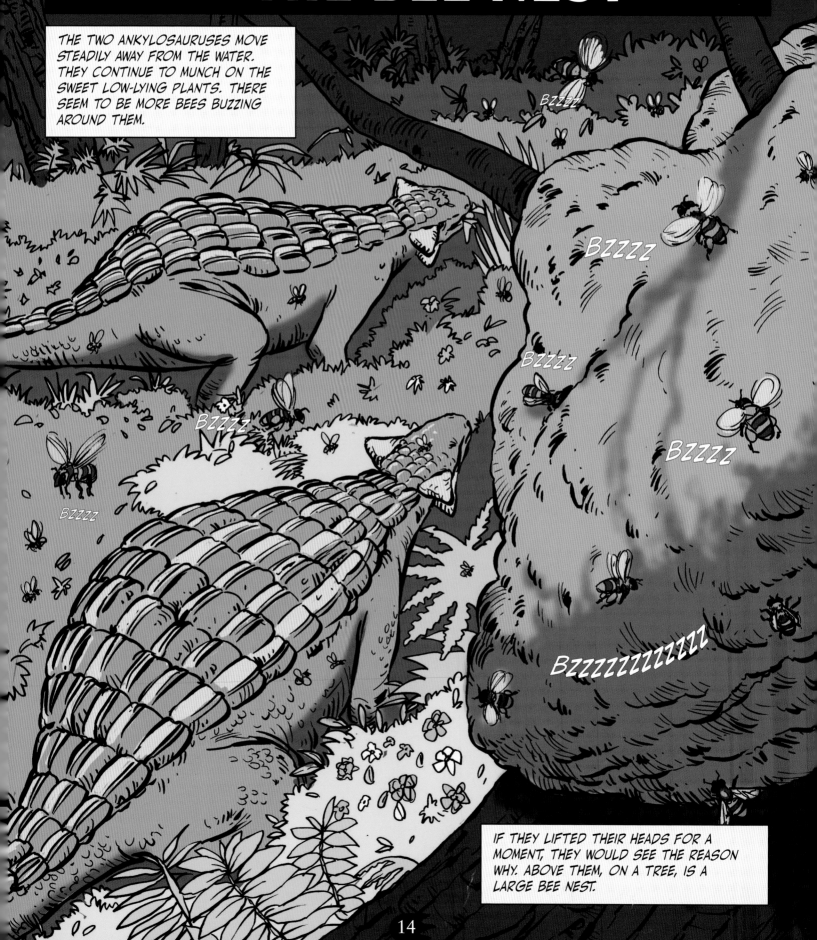

PART TWO... THE BEE NEST

THE TWO ANKYLOSAURUSES MOVE STEADILY AWAY FROM THE WATER. THEY CONTINUE TO MUNCH ON THE SWEET LOW-LYING PLANTS. THERE SEEM TO BE MORE BEES BUZZING AROUND THEM.

Bzzzz

Bzzzz

Bzzzz

Bzzzz

Bzzzz

Bzzzz

Bzzzzzzzzzzzz

IF THEY LIFTED THEIR HEADS FOR A MOMENT, THEY WOULD SEE THE REASON WHY. ABOVE THEM, ON A TREE, IS A LARGE BEE NEST.

NEARBY IS THE ROTTING **CARCASS** OF A PARASAUROLOPHUS, A DUCK-BILLED PLANT-EATING DINOSAUR WITH A LONG BONY HEAD CREST. IT HAS BEEN HALF EATEN AND IT STINKS.

SUDDENLY THERE IS A LOUD ROAR FROM CLOSE BY.

GWAAAAARRR!

THE GROUND IS SHAKEN BY THE FOOTSTEPS OF A LARGE BEAST.

THE TWO ANKYLOSAURUSES STOP EATING AND LOOK UP.

ABOVE THEM A LARGE FEMALE TYRANNOSAURUS APPEARS. SHE SMELLS THE CARCASS OF THE PARASAUROLOPHUS AND SHE IS VERY HUNGRY.

BROOAARRGH

THE NEARSIGHTED OLD BULL MISTAKENLY THINKS HE IS UNDER ATTACK AND TAKES UP A DEFENSIVE POSITION. ACCIDENTALLY, HE HAS PUT HIMSELF AND THE YOUNGSTER BETWEEN THE TYRANNOSAURUS AND HER MEAL.

ROAARRR

THE YOUNG ANKYLOSAURUS HIDES BEHIND THE OLD BULL.

THE OLD ANKYLOSAURUS WAVES HIS TAIL CLUB IN THE AIR.

GRAAARGH

GRUNT

BUT THE TYRANNOSAURUS IS TOO HUNGRY TO BACK OFF.

BROOAARRGH

SHE LUNGES AT THE OLD BULL WITH HER KNIFELIKE TEETH.

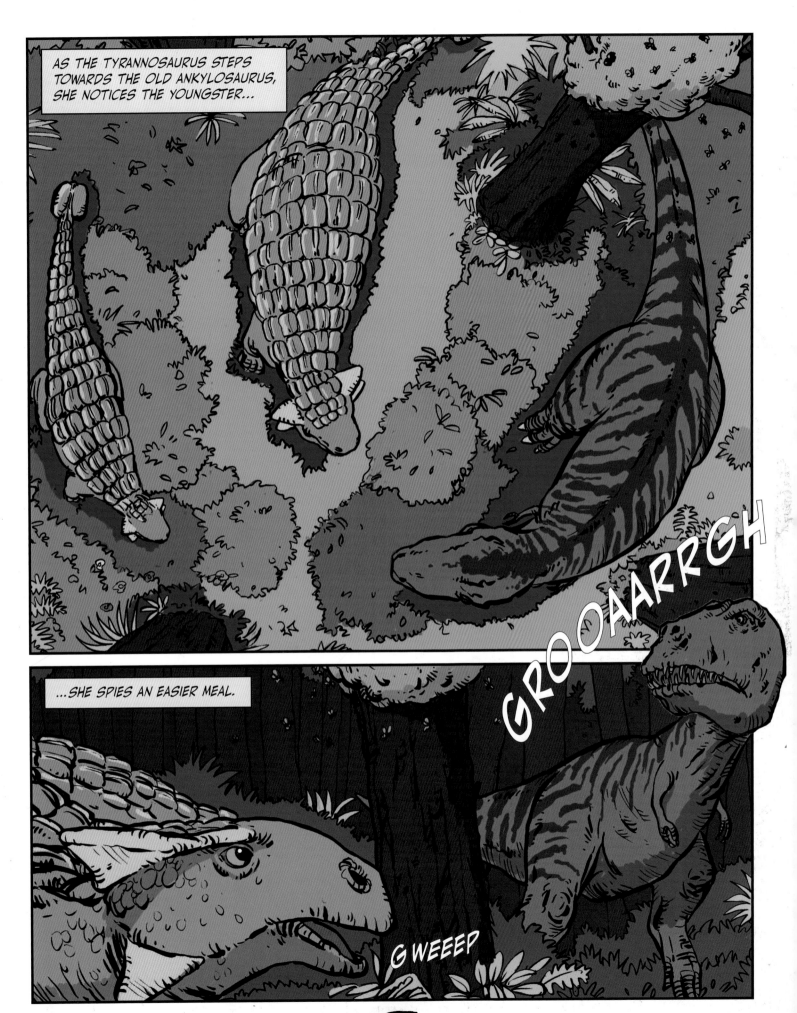

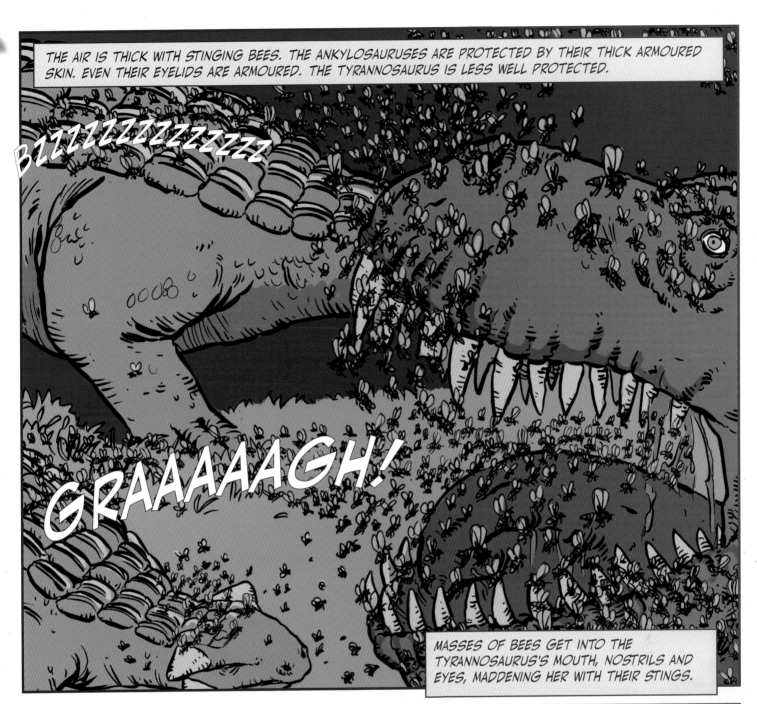

THE AIR IS THICK WITH STINGING BEES. THE ANKYLOSAURUSES ARE PROTECTED BY THEIR THICK ARMOURED SKIN. EVEN THEIR EYELIDS ARE ARMOURED. THE TYRANNOSAURUS IS LESS WELL PROTECTED.

BZZZZZZZZZZZZ

GRAAAAAGH!

MASSES OF BEES GET INTO THE TYRANNOSAURUS'S MOUTH, NOSTRILS AND EYES, MADDENING HER WITH THEIR STINGS.

THE TWO ANKYLOSAURUSES WATCH THE TYRANNOSAURUS TAKE OFF, FOLLOWED BY A CLOUD OF ANGRY BEES.

THE YOUNGSTER STAYS CLEAR OF THE BATTLING PACHYCEPHALOSAURUSES. HE WANDERS ALONG THE EDGE OF THE FOREST AND FINDS SOME PLANTS TO FEED ON. THE LOUD THUMPS STOP.

THE PACHYCEPHALOSAURUSES SCATTER AS A GROUP OF TRICERATOPS LUMBER PAST THEM. THE TRICERATOPS HEAD TOWARDS THE ANKYLOSAURUS, LOOKING FOR THE COOL SHADE OF THE TREES.

THE ANKYLOSAURUS IS WELL HIDDEN AMONGST THE PLANTS AND THE TRICERATOPS DO NOT SEE HIM.

BRRRAAAAGH

DAZED BUT UNHURT, THE YOUNGSTER HAS LANDED ON HIS BACK. HE IS IN BIG TROUBLE. HE HAS ENDED UP RIGHT NEXT TO A TYRANNOSAURUS NEST.

UP ON THE BANK OF THE HOLLOW, THE MOTHER HAS NOTICED HIM. SHE SEES THE ANKYLOSAURUS AS A DANGER TO HER EGGS.

GRRRRRRR

THE STRUGGLING ANKYLOSAURUS IS UNABLE TO ROLL ONTO HIS FEET. WITHIN A FEW SECONDS, THE TYRANNOSAURUS WILL REACH THE YOUNGSTER. HIS UNARMOURED UNDERSIDE HAS NO PROTECTION AGAINST HER SHARP TEETH.

PART FOUR... THE COMET

DEEP IN SPACE, THE ICY COMET CONTINUES ON ITS PATH, NARROWLY MISSING THE PLANET EARTH. A PIECE OF THE COMET HAS BROKEN OFF THOUGH AND IS BEING PULLED TOWARDS EARTH BY THE PLANET'S GRAVITATIONAL FORCE.

THIS FRAGMENT IS THE SIZE OF A HOUSE. IT IS MOVING AT OVER 160,934 KILOMETRES PER HOUR.

THE FRAGMENT OF COMET HURTLES THROUGH THE EARTH'S ATMOSPHERE, LEAVING A TRAIL OF WHITE VAPOUR.

WHISSSHHHHH

EIGHT KILOMETRES ABOVE EARTH'S SURFACE, IT EXPLODES WITH ENOUGH FORCE TO BE FELT OVER 2,590 SQUARE KILOMETRES.

BADOOOOM

THE SHOCK WAVE FROM THE EXPLOSION FLATTENS EVERYTHING IN ITS PATH.

PLANTS AND ANIMALS CLOSE TO THE EXPLOSION ARE DESTROYED.

THE YOUNG ANKYLOSAURUS SEES A WHITE FLASH. THEN HE FEELS THE EARTH TREMBLING AND HEARS A TERRIFYING RUMBLING SOUND.

THE TYRANNOSAURUS ON THE BANK, ALONG WITH EVERYTHING ELSE, IS BLOWN AWAY IN A POWERFUL BLAST.

KRAK!

IN THE HOLLOW, THE ANKYLOSAURUS IS PROTECTED FROM THE BLAST. THE SHAKING GROUND JOLTS THE YOUNGSTER TO HIS FEET AND HE COWERS AS ROCKS AND STONES FALL DOWN AROUND HIM.

FINALLY THE WIND AND THE SHAKING STOP. THE ANKYLOSAURUS HAS SURVIVED AND HE LOOKS AROUND AT A SCENE OF DESTRUCTION.

A BEE BUZZES PAST AND THE SWEET SMELL OF PLANTS REACHES HIM. THE ANKYLOSAURUS IS HUNGRY AND HE WALKS OFF IN SEARCH OF FOOD.

FOSSIL EVIDENCE

WE CAN GET A GOOD IDEA OF WHAT DINOSAURS MAY HAVE LOOKED LIKE FROM THEIR FOSSILS. FOSSILS ARE FORMED WHEN THE HARD PARTS OF AN ANIMAL OR PLANT ARE BURIED AND THEN TURN INTO ROCK OVER MILLIONS OF YEARS.

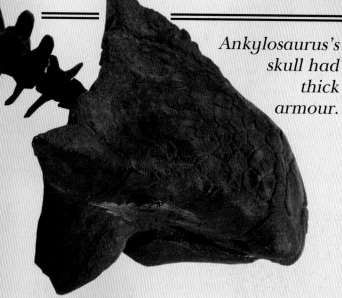

Ankylosaurus's skull had thick armour.

Fossils of Ankylosaurus have been found in rock formations dating to the very end of the Cretaceous period in western North America. Although a complete skeleton has never been discovered, several parts, such as the head, skin and tail club, have been dug up. The famous tail club of Ankylosaurus was made of several large osteoderms, which were joined to the last few tailbones. These tailbones formed a stiff rod at the base of the club. Thick **tendons**, which were attached to the tailbones have been preserved.

These tendons were part bone and were not very elastic. This allowed a great force to be sent to the end of the tail when it was swung. It was probably a very good defensive weapon, capable of producing enough impact to break the bones of an attacker. It has also been suggested that the tail club acted as a pretend head to fool an attacker, although this idea is generally no longer accepted.

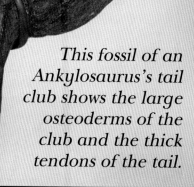

This fossil of an Ankylosaurus's tail club shows the large osteoderms of the club and the thick tendons of the tail.

ANIMAL GALLERY

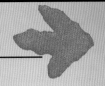

ALL THESE ANIMALS APPEAR IN THE STORY.

 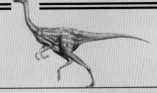 

Ichthyornis
(ick-thee-OR-niss)
'Fish bird'
Wingspan: 65 centimetres
A seabird with a toothed beak.

Ornithomimus
(orn-ITH-oh-MEE-mus)
'Bird mimic'
Length: 4 metres
A fast-running, meat-eating
dinosaur with a bony,
toothless beak.

Pachycephalosaurus
(pack-i-KEF-al-oh-sore-russ)
'Thick-headed lizard'
Length: 5.5 metres
A plant eater with a very thick
and bony skull.

Parasaurolophus
(pa-ra-saw-ROL-off-us)
'Near crested lizard'
Length: 10 metres
A plant-eating dinosaur with a long, tube-shaped
head crest and a duckbill-like mouth.

Triceratops
(tri-SERRA-tops)
'Three-horned face'
Length: 8 – 9 metres
A plant-eating dinosaur with a large bony
frill and three horns.

Tyrannosaurus (tie-RAN-oh-sore-us)
'Tyrant lizard'
Length: 12 metres
A huge, meat-eating dinosaur weighing over
5,443 kilogrammes.

Deinosuchus (DINE-oh-SUE-kus)
'Terrible crocodile'
Length: 12 metres
A giant, extinct relative of the alligator capable
of killing and eating large dinosaurs.

GLOSSARY

carcass	The dead body of an animal.
comet	A ball of ice and dust in space that leaves a trail of gas.
Cretaceous period	The period of time between 145 million and 65 million years ago.
extinction	When the last member of a group of any living things has died out.
fossils	The remains of living things that have turned to rock.
meteor	A rock from space that falls to Earth.
osteoderms	Bony parts in the skin.
pollinating	The movement of pollen to reproduce.
prey	Animals that are hunted for food by another animal.
tendons	The stringy parts that connect bone to muscles.

INDEX